In this comic ...

Batman is one of the Super Friends.

Aquaman is king of the seas.

Captain Fear is a lost sailor.

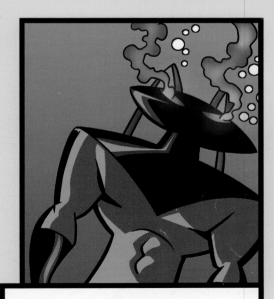

Black Manta is a crook.

The Super Friends were at sea. Suddenly, an odd sound echoed around them.

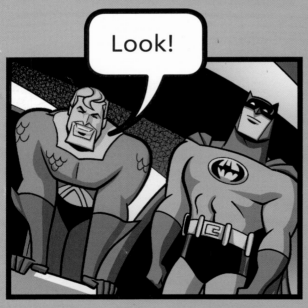

3

5

8

10

Captain Fear hurls a rock at the stone.

Crack!

Fool! You have broken the Stone of Skood.

But my friends are safe.

The stone is in bits.